THE WONDER BOOK OF SEX

GLEN BAXTER

A doctor comments:

*'After years of exhaustive research
I can honestly say that the arrival of
this volume marks the climax of my career!'*

LITTLE, BROWN AND COMPANY
Boston · New York · Toronto · London

CONTENTS

THE PATHWAY TO SEXUAL ECSTASY

RECOGNITION

LEARNING TO RECOGNIZE THE OPPOSITE SEX

HIDDEN GUSSETS

FOR SOME, THE USE OF SPECIALIZED
EQUIPMENT MAY BE NECESSARY

EROGENOUS ZONES

SOMETIMES THE SEARCH
TO LOCATE THEM MAY WELL PROVE
TO BE AN ULTIMATELY
UNREWARDING EXPERIENCE

SEXUAL PREFERENCE

IT IS IMPORTANT TO ENSURE YOUR SEXUAL PREFERENCES COINCIDE WITH THOSE OF YOUR PARTNER

A doctor says: *'... especially if one of you is American.'*

A doctor says:

'There are, of course any number of occasions when a knowledge of webbing and oil-based adhesives is a positive advantage.'

LOOK FOR TELLTALE SIGNS THAT MAY LEAD YOU TO COME TO TERMS WITH THE EROTIC NEEDS OF YOUR PARTNER

HINTS & TIPS

A SHARED INTEREST IN LINOLEUM
CAN BE A
SIGNIFICANT SEXUAL TURN ON

A doctor says:

'Nowadays many people from a variety of different backgrounds are expressing an interest in a healthier lifestyle.'

"THE BRUSSELS SWIRL"

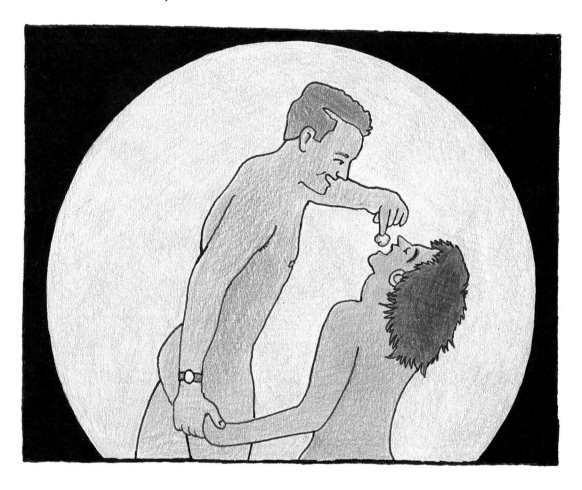

FOR MANY COUPLES THE FIRST SENSUAL TOUCH OF A PAR-BOILED SPROUT AS A PRELUDE TO LOVEMAKING IS A SENSATION THEY WILL NEVER FORGET

THE ANTWERP POSITION

FOR SOME REASON VERY POPULAR IN
TEDDINGTON, THIS PARTICULAR MANOEUVRE
TRADITIONALLY UTILISES A PEWTER
CHAIN, OVEN MITTS AND A RUFF.
THE JEWELLED GARTER IS OPTIONAL

THE SO-CALLED "GERMAN TECHNIQUE"

ITS ORIGIN OBSCURED IN BAVARIAN MYTH, THIS TECHNIQUE USUALLY INVOLVES A TRAPEZE, A SILK SCARF, A TUMBLER OF SCHNAPPS (RICE VINEGAR CAN BE SUBSTITUTED HERE) AND 240 GRAMS OF SALTPETRE AND SAUERKRAUT.

(WOAD IS OPTIONAL)

A doctor says:

'The upsurge of interest in tweed seems to reflect a growing concern for many young couples.'

THE "TELEGRAPH AND ARGUS" POSITION,
ONCE FAVOURED EXCLUSIVELY BY DENIZENS
OF THE NORTH OF ENGLAND IS NOW ALMOST
FASHIONABLE IN THE BODMIN AREA

FOR SOME COUPLES THE INTRODUCTION
OF FRESH FRUIT INTO THEIR DAILY
ROUTINE HAS ADDED A WELCOME
EXTRA DIMENSION OF PLEASURE

STEP
4

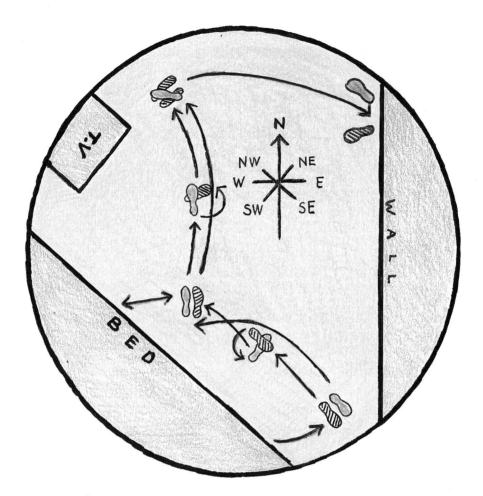

SOME OF THE MORE ADVANCED
LOVEMAKING POSITIONS CAN PROVE
TO BE POTENTIALLY FATAL. IT IS
PRUDENT THEREFORE TO CONSIDER
CARRYING DETAILED MAPS OF ALL
THE BUILDINGS YOU MAY FREQUENT

A doctor says:

'For some people a wrinkle-proof
knapsack can prove invaluable here.'

IN THE PAST, BEFORE THE AMENDMENT
TO THE HIGHWAYS, GOLF COURSE AND
SHRUBBERY ACT OF 1953, MERELY BEING
SEEN OUTDOORS WITH A MEMBER OF THE
OPPOSITE SEX WAS TECHNICALLY AN
OFFENCE AND MANY COUPLES WALKED
IN FEAR OF APPREHENSION BY THE VICE
SQUAD, HAVING THEIR NAMES AND ADDRESSES
TAKEN DOWN ON ONE OF THE INFAMOUS PINK
SLIPS WHICH WOULD LATER BE PUBLISHED
IN THE WEEKLY "JOURNAL OF SHAME" AND
DISPLAYED ON THE SHELVES OF LEADING
NEWSAGENTS AND MILLINERS
THROUGHOUT THE LAND.

HOWEVER, DESPITE A MORE LIBERAL
APPROACH BEING ADOPTED BY THE
POLICE IN RESPECT OF NOCTURNAL
OUTDOOR LIASONS, THE SITUATION
REMAINS FRAUGHT WITH DANGER,
AS ONE UNFORTUNATE SUITOR
DISCOVERED TO HIS COST JUST EIGHT
MILES SOUTH EAST OF BICESTER

"I'M AFRAID I'M GOING TO HAVE TO
SHOW YOU MY NIPPLE, YOUNG LAD"
ANNOUNCED THE CONSTABLE GRAVELY

NOWADAYS A MUCH MORE RELAXED
ATTITUDE TO AL FRESCO DALLIANCE
PREVAILS AND MANY COUPLES ARE
ABLE TO ENJOY EACH OTHER'S
COMPANY IN THE RELATIVE
SECLUSION OF THEIR FAVOURITE SPOT

A doctor says:

'Many people have a passion for gorse and heather. However, in my opinion some of the more strenuous pursuits currently on offer should not be attempted by the over-45 group.'

DESPITE THE VARIED ATTRACTIONS
OF OUTDOOR SEX, MOST COUPLES
STILL PREFER THE WARMTH AND
SECLUSION OF A DOMESTIC SETTING

SEX IN EUROPE

A doctor speaks about Belgian sex:

'Belgium seems to be the butt of a thousand jokes. This is patently unfair. Belgians are normal, hard-working people. In an attempt to redress the balance, here is a picture of two young Belgians enjoying an evening of uninhibited sex.'

A doctor says:

'The Germans, of course, have adopted a much more pragmatic approach to lovemaking.'

IN MUNICH, DEXTERITY WITH SMALL VEGETABLES IS VALUED MORE HIGHLY THAN SEXUAL PROWESS.

THERE ARE MANY WHO SEEK
SEXUAL FULFILMENT

ON PUBLIC TRANSPORT

STEP 7

THE SWISS WERE AMONGST THE FIRST TO RECOGNIZE THE IMPORTANCE OF SAFE SEX

LAWS WERE PASSED MAKING THE WEARING OF BOBBLE HATS AND SENSIBLE FOOTWEAR COMPULSORY AT ALTITUDES ABOVE 114 METRES

A Swiss doctor says:

'Although great emphasis is generally placed on the importance of timing, it should never be regarded solely as the ultimate goal.'

SEX OLYMPICS

UNFORTUNATELY THE GAMES SCHEDULED FOR SUMMER 1995 HAD TO BE CANCELLED FOLLOWING THE COLLAPSE OF DOCTOR A.E. LIRKETT'S BUNGALOW IN HILVERSUM DURING A LATE SPRING TRAINING PROGRAMME. ALTHOUGH CONSIDERABLE DAMAGE WAS INFLICTED ON THE FABRIC OF THE BUILDING, DOCTOR LIRKETT, TWO ZEBRAS, A MOORHEN, A 17TH CENTURY CHINESE URN AND A FRUITMOTH ALL MANAGED TO ESCAPE UNSCATHED.

BONDAGE

ONCE CONSIDERED A TABOO SUBJECT
BY MANY, BONDAGE HAS RECENTLY BEEN
EXPERIENCING A RENAISSANCE
FOLLOWING THE ENORMOUS SUCCESS
OF FILMS LIKE "HARRIET VISITS
NORWICH FOR THE DAY" AND
"MAKE MINE BROCCOLI"

FOR SOME THE PATHWAY TO ORGASMIC BLISS IS NOT ENTIRELY A BED OF ROSES

A doctor says:

'Dieppe twine, once a popular item in Wales, has recently lost favour since the notorious Draper's Court incident in May 1996.'

BONDAGE CAN BE A HIGHLY DANGEROUS
ACTIVITY. ALWAYS SEEK ADVICE FROM
THOSE YOU KNOW AND TRUST BEFORE
EMBARKING ON AN EVENING OF PLEASURE

LOCATING THE G-SPOT

IN 1946 THE GERMAN OBSTETRICIAN AND GYNAECOLOGIST ERNEST GRÄFENBERG DESCRIBED A ZONE OF EROGENOUS FEELING

MEN ALL OVER THE WORLD HAVE BEEN LOOKING FOR IT EVER SINCE...

A doctor speaks:

'... with varying degrees of success.'

ORAL SEX

ORAL SEX OFFERS A BLEND OF INTIMACY GENEROSITY, TENDERNESS AND TRUST

THE POPULAR "DUNDEE POSITION"

SEXUAL TABOOS

A) BIVALVE INTERFERENCE

B) UNDER-ARM HAIR

ONCE CONSIDERED A SEXUAL
TURN-OFF, BUT RECENTLY
RECLAIMED BY RADICAL
GROUPS AS AN EROTIC
FEATURE, IS NOW VERY
POPULAR IN NORFOLK AND
THE SOUTH CROYDON AREA

APHRODISIACS

A doctor says:

'The latest E.E.C. regulations have made the acquisition of large quantities of gherkins for personal consumption totally legal.'

IN POITIERS, POWDERED GHERKIN IS HIGHLY REGARDED AS A POWERFUL APHRODISIAC AND FORMS THE BASIS OF THE STAPLE DIET OF THE LOCAL ANTIQUARIAN BOOKSELLERS.

IN SOME REMOTE PARTS OF PERU
EVEN AN OBLIQUE REFERENCE TO

THE SURFACE TEXTURE OF A GHERKIN
OFTEN RESULTS IN SPONTANEOUS
ERUPTIONS OF EROTIC PLEASURE

A doctor says:

'*For many couples the old method of aubergine anorak withdrawal is now happily a thing of the past.*'

FETISHISM

DESPITE THE RESURGENCE OF INTEREST
IN SILK, SATIN AND RUBBER, MANY
YOUNG COUPLES KEEP RETURNING
TO THE TRADITIONAL MATERIALS
FOR THEIR EROTIC PLEASURE

A doctor says:

'However, sudden changes in the landscape south of Durham have indicated significant new trends.'

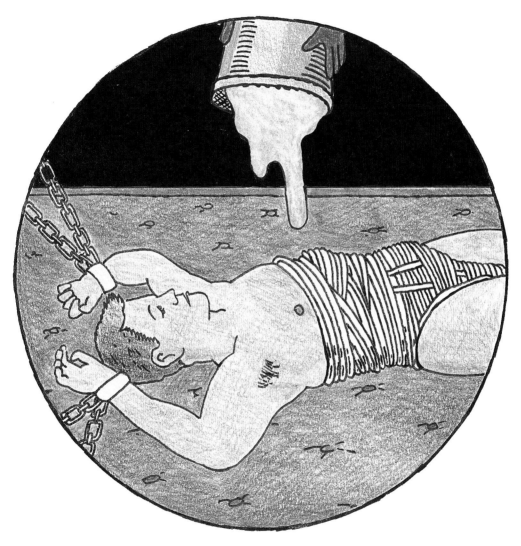

IN MANY HOUSEHOLDS THROUGHOUT THE UNITED KINGDOM RESEARCH SHOWS THAT GUACAMOLE IS GRADUALLY REPLACING GREEK STYLE YOGHURT AS THE RELISH OF CHOICE

IN ORDER TO COPE WITH INCREASED DEMAND
1995 HAS SEEN THE GROWTH OF A NUMBER
OF NEW CLUBS DESIGNED TO CATER FOR
THOSE WITH SPECIFIC SEXUAL NEEDS. ONE
SUCH CLUB IN THE CENTRE OF HULL NOW
BOASTS PARKING FACILITIES FOR 800 CARS

EROTICISM IN THE HOME

SOMETIMES EVEN UNLIKELY OBJECTS
AND HOUSEHOLD ITEMS APPEAR TO
EMIT POTENT EROTIC SIGNALS

FIG A THE BLACK OLIVE

FIG B BROWN SHOELACES

FIG C DANDRUFF

MASTURBATION (FEMALE)

UNTIL QUITE RECENTLY A TABOO SUBJECT.
FORTUNATELY A COMPLETE RANGE OF
SPECIALIST CLOTHING IS NOW GENERALLY
AVAILABLE THROUGHOUT EUROPE

MASTURBATION (MALE)

ONCE THOUGHT TO CAUSE INSANITY, RHEUMATISM AND ACNE, THIS RECREATION HAS LED TO THE ERECTION OF NUMEROUS CLUBS IN CENTRAL LONDON WHERE THE SUBJECT IS THOROUGHLY ADDRESSED

BODY DECORATION

NUMBER ONE – THE PENIS

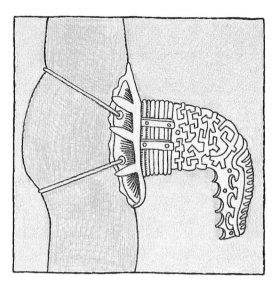

'THE MACCLESFIELD'

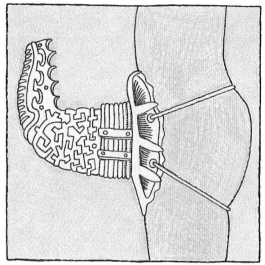

'THE EXETER'

SHELLS, HORN, BASKETRY, BARK, LINOLEUM AND BAMBOO ARE TRADITIONALLY EMPLOYED TO ACCENTUATE THE MALE SEXUAL ORGAN. COLOURED PIGMENTS ARE OFTEN USED TO GREAT EFFECT. THIS CAN HOWEVER BE QUITE PAINFUL AND GENERALLY SUPPLIERS OF SUCH PIGMENTS DO RECOMMEND LIGHT SANDING AND THE APPLICATION OF A MATT GREY UNDERCOAT BEFORE THE FINAL DECORATION IS PUT IN PLACE

IN SAMOA AND CERTAIN PARTS OF
COTTINGLEY, THE ELBOW IS CONSIDERED
TO BE THE ULTIMATE EROTIC ZONE
AND IS THE SUBJECT OF CONSTANT
NOCTURNAL SURVEILLANCE

SEX GADGETS & APPLIANCES

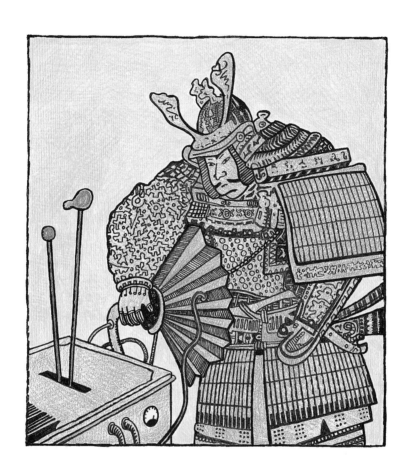

A doctor speaks:

'Some of the latest virtual reality sex aids from Japan seem to be making a big impact on the British market.'

ALTHOUGH BRITISH PRODUCTS STILL SEEM TO BE HOLDING THEIR OWN AT THE LUXURY END OF A FIERCELY COMPETITIVE WORLD MARKET

STEP 18

A doctor says:

'Some of the more sophisticated appliances currently available need to be handled very carefully. It is advisable to have a qualified electrician standing by.'

BEWARE MEN
WITH
SUGGESTIVE
TATTOOS

AND THOSE WITH
AN UNHEALTHY
INTEREST
IN CAMPANOLOGY

SAFE SEX

ALWAYS MAKE SURE THAT ADEQUATE PRECAUTIONS ARE TAKEN

A LITTLE, BROWN BOOK

First published in Great Britain in 1995 by Little, Brown and Company (UK)

A CIP catalogue record for the book is available from the British Library

ISBN 0-316-87531-7

10 9 8 7 6 5 4 3 2 1

Designed by David Fordham

Printed and bound in Italy by New Interlitho

Little, Brown and Company (UK)
Brettenham House, Lancaster Place, London WC2E 7EN